First published 1998
Text & Illustrations © Wooden Books Ltd 1998

Published by Wooden Books Ltd.
Walkmill, Cascob, Presteigne, Powys, Wales LD8 2NT

British Library Cataloguing in Publication Data
Abu-Asiya, Dawud, 1972-
Platonic and Archimedean Solids

A CIP catalogue record for this book is
available from the British Library

ISBN 1 902418 03 4

Printed in Great Britain
by Redwood Books Ltd,
Trowbridge, Wiltshire, UK.

PLATONIC AND ARCHIMEDEAN SOLIDS

written and illustrated by

Dawud Abu-Asiya

In The Name of God,
The Compassionate, The Merciful.

CONTENTS

Unfolding From Unity

―――――――――――

Imagine a point.

From this point, extend a line.

Rotate this line about the point to trace a circle.

Rotate this circle about the point to make a sphere.

The sphere is a unity; every point on its surface is identical to every other. It contains an infinite number of potential forms. As the sphere uncovers its potential and the forms crystallise, beautiful interrelationships are revealed.

This small book charts the unfolding of number in three-dimensional space through the most fundamental solid forms contained in the sphere.

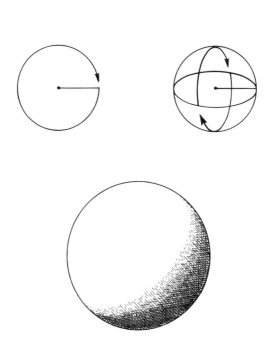

DIVISIONS OF THE SPHERE

There are only five ways to divide the surface of a sphere into identical sections that have equal edges and equal angles.

These regular divisions are into four, six, eight, twelve and twenty sections.

Each of these ways has a unique character, and is beautiful in its simplicity.

Mankind has known of these five regular divisions of a sphere at least since neolithic times.

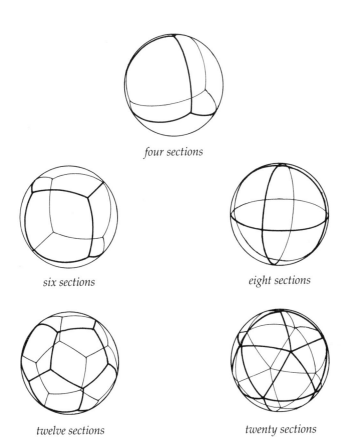

four sections

six sections

eight sections

twelve sections

twenty sections

The Platonic Solids

Joining the points that define the five regular divisions of the sphere with straight lines instead of curves traces out five solid forms. These solids fit perfectly inside the sphere, every corner, or vertex, just touching it. They are the only solids possible that have every face, edge and vertex identical.

The Greeks named these five solids by the number of their faces. The solid with four faces is known as the tetrahedron; *tetra* means four, and *hedron* means 'bases'. The others are the hexahedron, or cube, with six faces, the octahedron with eight faces, the dodecahedron with twelve faces, and the icosahedron with twenty faces.

Nowadays they are commonly referred to as the Platonic solids because Plato explained them in his Timaeus. He assigned four to the elements: Fire (tetrahedron), Air (octahedron), Water (icosahedron) and Earth (hexahedron). The fifth solid, the dodecahedron, was assigned to the heavens.

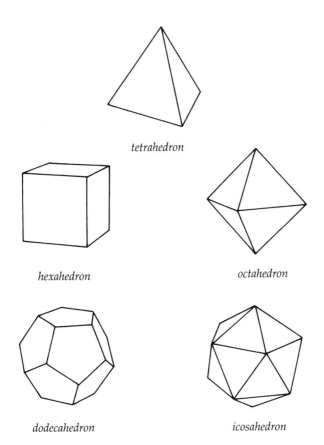

tetrahedron

hexahedron

octahedron

dodecahedron

icosahedron

THE ELEMENTS

In Plato's creation story the primary distinction is between Fire and Earth. Fire is light, Earth is solid. Thus the universe becomes visible and tangible. To prevent Fire and Earth separating completely, the intermediary elements of Air and Water are required to bind them together.

Fire is hot and dry, Air is hot and moist, Water is cold and moist, Earth is cold and dry. The moisture, or fluidity, of Air and Water makes life possible.

The elements are understood as occupying four concentric spheres.

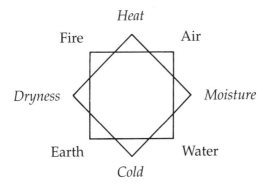

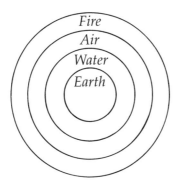

THE TETRAHEDRON

4 faces : 6 edges : 4 vertices

The tetrahedron is the simplest three-dimensional form after the sphere. Its four faces are all equilateral triangles; three triangles meet at every vertex. Every vertex of the tetrahedron is perpendicular to the centre of the opposite face (*below*).

The tetrahedron is associated with the element of Fire. It is from this association that we get the word pyramid, the Greek for fire being *pyros*.

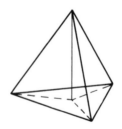

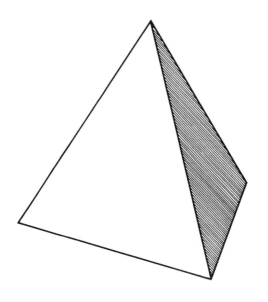

TETRAHEDRAL SYMMETRY

When viewed edge on, the tetrahedron can be divided into two identical halves. If rotated through half a full turn it will appear the same as in its starting position. This is known as a two-fold symmetry.

Face on, the tetrahedron has a three-fold symmetry; one third of a full turn leaves it appearing as it started. It also has a three-fold symmetry when viewed from a vertex.

It is interesting that the tetrahedron, which is made entirely of triangles, makes a square from one of these views.

The symmetry diagrams in this book show in dotted line any edges that would otherwise be concealed by the upper faces of the solid. For example, the dotted line in the 'edge on' diagram opposite is the edge at the back of this view of the tetrahedron.

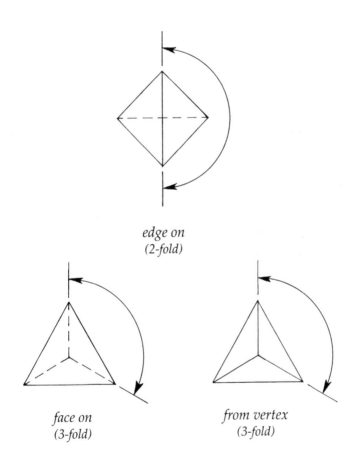

edge on
(2-fold)

face on
(3-fold)

from vertex
(3-fold)

THE OCTAHEDRON

8 faces : 12 edges : 6 vertices

The faces of the regular octahedron are all equilateral triangles with four faces meeting at every vertex. It is associated with the element of Air. The structures of many crystals are based on the octahedron.

Edge on, the octahedron becomes a diamond, or rhombus. Face on, a six pointed Star of David appears. The view from a vertex is a quartered square.

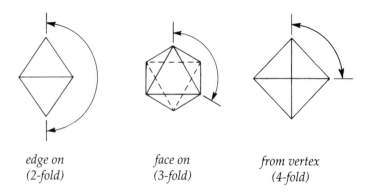

edge on
(2-fold)

face on
(3-fold)

from vertex
(4-fold)

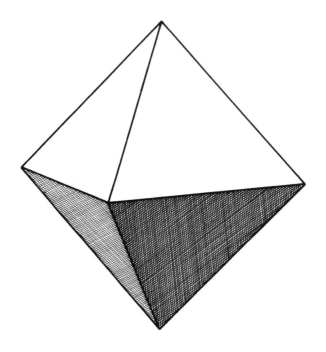

A CURIOUS HARMONY

The ratio that determines the musical interval of an octave is 1:2. If a tuned string is divided in half the new note produced is one octave higher than the original note.

When the halfway divisions, or midpoints, of the edges of a regular tetrahedron are joined together the result is an octahedron. The edge length of this octahedron is half that of the tetrahedron. The octahedron is a kind of octave harmony of the tetrahedron.

Notice how four small tetrahedra are also traced out surrounding the octahedron.

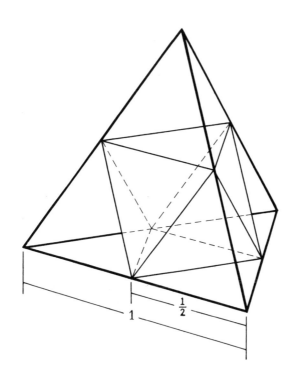

THE ICOSAHEDRON

20 faces : 30 edges : 12 vertices

The icosahedron is made of equilateral triangles. Five triangles meet at every vertex. The icosahedron is associated with the element of Water. Water is life. Five-fold symmetry, like that of the icosahedron, occurs in nature almost exclusively in living organisms.

Edge on, the icosahedron makes a curious squashed hexagon. Face on, a regular hexagon surrounds a Star of David. From a vertex a ten pointed star appears.

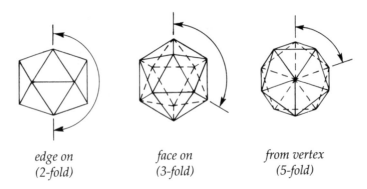

edge on
(2-fold)

face on
(3-fold)

from vertex
(5-fold)

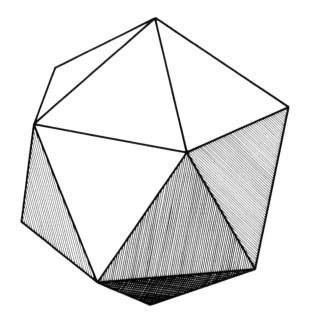

A UNIQUE PROPORTION

There is only one way to divide a line such that the shorter section is to the longer as the longer section is to the whole line.

If the shorter section is one then the longer section is the square root of five plus one, divided by two (approximately 1.618). This is known as the golden number and is represented by the Greek letter ϕ (phi). If the longer section is one then the whole line is ϕ.

A golden rectangle has sides of one and ϕ. If a one by one square is removed from one side, the rectangle left is also a golden rectangle. This process can continue indefinitely, and defines the golden spiral.

ϕ is innately related to five-fold symmetry. If the edge of a pentagon is one then its diagonal is ϕ. Marking out a pentagon star then divides this diagonal into the golden ratio.

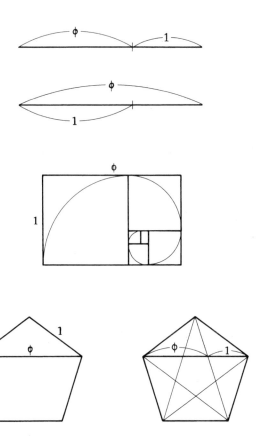

An Elegant Juxtaposition

The edges of the icosahedron form fifteen pairs of parallel lines. If a pair of these parallel lines is joined together, the result is a golden rectangle (*below left*).

The twelve vertices of the icosahedron can be located using three golden rectangles set at right angles to each other (*opposite*). Related to this is the icosahedron inside a cube (*below right*). All twelve vertices of the icosahedron lie on the faces of the cube and if the edge of the icosahedron is one, then the edge of the cube is ϕ.

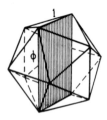

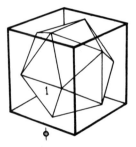

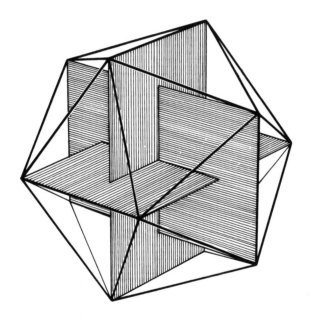

A GOLDEN NEST

The icosahedron fits perfectly within the octahedron, with eight of the icosahedron's faces on the faces of the octahedron.

Once the two solids are snugly nested in this way, the twelve vertices of the icosahedron touch the twelve edges of the octahedron.

The point where each vertex touches an edge divides it into the ratio of 1:φ, the golden ratio.

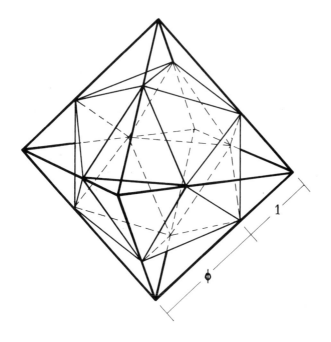

THE CUBE

6 faces : 12 edges : 8 vertices

The cube is associated with the element of Earth. Edge on, it forms two rectangles, from a vertex, six triangles make a hexagon, and face on, a more predictable square comes into view.

The world's most famous cube is the Kaaba, literally 'cube', in Mecca. The sanctuary of the temple of Solomon was also a cube. A cube faces forwards, backwards, left, right, up and down, establishing the six directions, North, South, East, West, the heavens and the Earth.

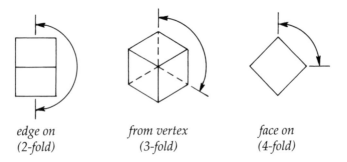

edge on
(2-fold)

from vertex
(3-fold)

face on
(4-fold)

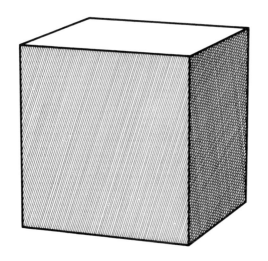

THE FIRE IN THE EARTH

A curious relationship exists between the regular tetrahedron and the cube. Take one diagonal from each face of the cube so that three diagonals meet at every vertex, and a regular tetrahedron is traced out (*opposite*). This is one way to depict the primary duality of Fire and Earth.

Since there are two diagonals for each face of the cube, there are two tetrahedra that fit inside the cube in this way. Together these two tetrahedra form the stella octangula (*below*).

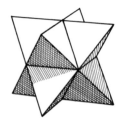

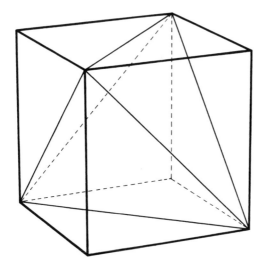

THE DODECAHEDRON

12 faces : 30 edges : 20 vertices

The twelve faces of the regular dodecahedron are all pentagons; three faces meet at every vertex. The edge on and vertex views of the dodecahedron produce rather odd shapes. Face on, an elegant ten-pointed star is surrounded by a decagon or ten-sided shape.

Plato says of the dodecahedron, "There remained a fifth construction, which God used for embroidering the constellations on the whole (spherical) heaven". The dodecahedron is the Platonic solid closest to a sphere.

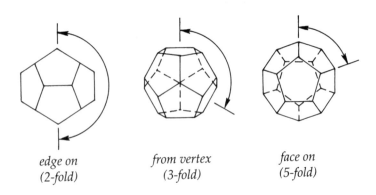

edge on
(2-fold)

from vertex
(3-fold)

face on
(5-fold)

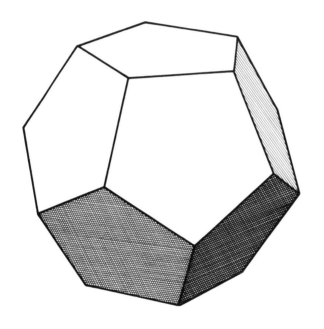

The Vault Of The Heavens

As the tetrahedron fits inside the cube (*see page 28*), so the cube fits inside the dodecahedron. Marking a diagonal on each face of the dodecahedron so that three meet at every vertex traces out a cube (*opposite*). If the edge length of this dodecahedron is one then the edge of the cube is φ.

There are five possible diagonals on each pentagonal face. How many earthly cubes can be traced out in a heavenly dodecahedron?

Every cube contains two fiery tetrahedra. How many tetrahedra fit inside a dodecahedron?

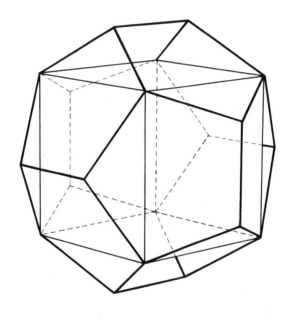

ALL THINGS IN PAIRS

Join the centres of the faces of a tetrahedron and another tetrahedron is traced out (*opposite*).

Join the centres of the faces of an octahedron and a cube is traced out. Joining the centres of this cube results in an octahedron (*page 36*). The same relationship exists between the icosahedron and the dodecahedron (*page 37*). Two solids related to each other in this way are known as each other's duals. The number of vertices on a solid equals the number of faces on its dual, and vice versa. Solids that are each other's duals have the same number of edges.

The tetrahedron is its own dual. The vertices of the tetrahedron point in four directions. The vertices of the the tetrahedron that is its dual point in the opposite directions.

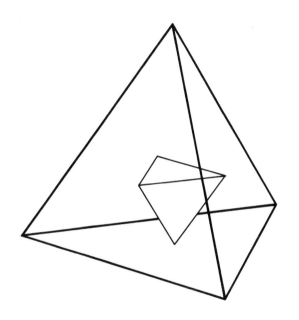

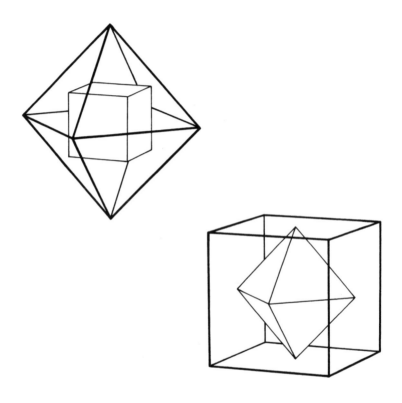

Everything in creation has its counterpart or opposite;
day and night, the Sun and the Moon, male and female,
the heavens and the Earth.

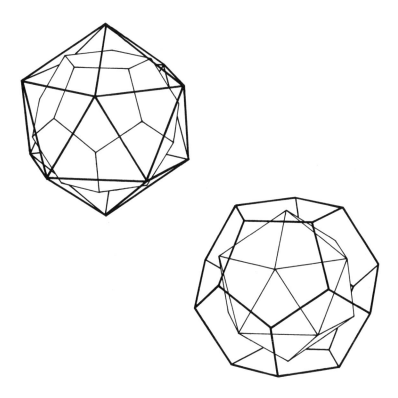

The relationships on these pages are beautiful examples of this principle, and also of the interdependence of opposites, each clothing and defining the other.

THE ARCHIMEDEAN SOLIDS

The thirteen Archimedean solids (named after the Greek mathematician Archimedes) are the next stage in the unfolding of the potential forms in the sphere. The Archimedean solids all fit perfectly inside a sphere, every vertex just touching the sphere's surface.

Each face of an Archimedean solid has equal edges and equal angles. The combination of faces around the vertices of an Archimedean solid is the same, but unlike the Platonic solids they each have more than one type of face. They are made using triangles, squares, pentagons (five sides), hexagons (six sides), octagons (eight sides), and decagons (ten sides).

All the Archimedean solids can be produced by transforming a Platonic solid through one or more stages. One is derived from the tetrahedron (top), six are derived from the octahedron or the cube (rows two and three), and six are derived from the icosahedron or the dodecahedron (rows four and five).

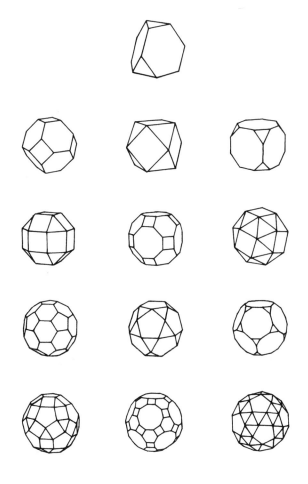

FIVE TRUNCATIONS

Cut the corners off the Platonic solids to produce five new equal edged solids that fit perfectly in a sphere. Clockwise from the top they are the truncated tetrahedron, the truncated octahedron, the truncated icosahedron, the truncated dodecahedron and the truncated cube.

The truncated octahedron can completely fill space with copies of itself. The only other Platonic or Archimedean solid that does this is the cube.

Each truncated solid sits neatly inside both its original Platonic solid and that solid's dual. For example, the truncated octahedron fits inside the octahedron and the cube.

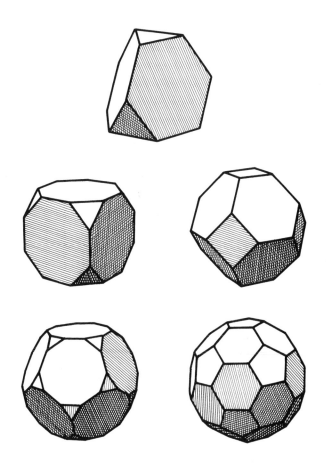

THE CUBOCTAHEDRON

14 faces : 24 edges : 12 vertices

The cuboctahedron can be thought of as a kind of combination of the octahedron and the cube. It has eight triangular faces and six square faces. The radius of the sphere around the cuboctahedron is the same as the cuboctahedron's edge length .

Joining the midpoints of the edges of an octahedron traces out a cuboctahedron (*below left*). Joining the midpoints of the edges of a cube has the same result (*below right*).

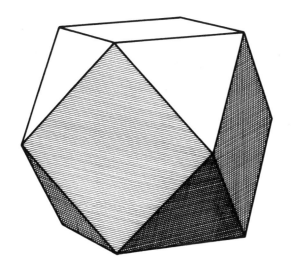

THE TWELVE DISCIPLES

The greatest number of identical spheres that fit around a central sphere, also identical, is twelve. This 'close-packing' can be visualised as a layer of seven spheres (six around a centre) with three spheres nesting on top and three spheres nesting underneath (top). If the centres of the twelve outer spheres are joined together a cuboctahedron is defined (bottom).

The archetype of twelve around a centre is fundamental: seen from the Earth the Sun travels through twelve zodiacal constellations, there were twelve tribes of Israel led by the Prophet Moses, Plato's ideal city was based on a twelve-fold plan, Jesus had twelve disciples, and the Prophet Muhammad said, "After me will come twelve amirs (representatives)".

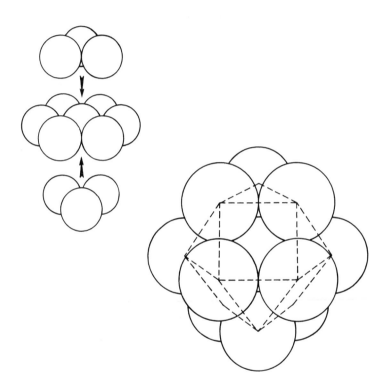

A Cunning Twist

Picture a cuboctahedron (*top left*) in which only the triangular faces are surfaces (*top right*).

This structure can twist in on itself. In so doing the square 'holes' become distorted; two opposite corners move further apart, the other two move closer together (*centre*).

When the distance between the closing corners is the same as the edge length of the triangles (*bottom left*), join these corners to define an icosahedron (*bottom right*).

The cuboctahedron combines the cube, or Earth, with the octahedron, or Air. It twists in on itself to become the icosahedron, which is Water, the element between Earth and Air.

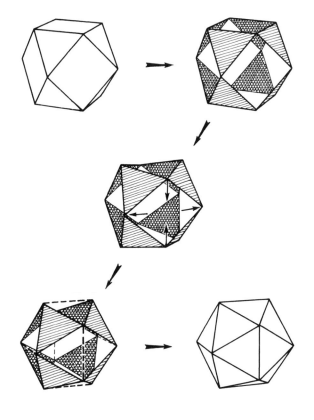

THE ICOSIDODECAHEDRON

32 faces : 60 edges : 30 vertices

The icosidodecahedron can be thought of as a kind of combination of the icosahedron and the dodecahedron. It has twenty triangular faces and twelve pentagonal faces.

The icosidodecahedron can be produced by joining the midpoints of the edges of the icosahedron (*below left*). It can also be produced by joining the midpoints of the edges of the dodecahedron (*below right*).

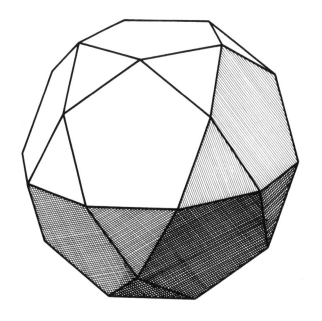

FOUR EXPLOSIONS

Four of the Archimedean solids are 'explosions' of other solids. Exploding the faces of a cube until separated by an edge length (*below*) defines the rhombicuboctahedron (*top left*). This solid is also an exploded octahedron. Exploding a dodecahedron or icosahedron makes the rhombicosidodecahedron (*top right*).

The main faces of the truncated cube or truncated octahedron explode to form the great rhombicuboctahedron (*bottom left*), those of the truncated dodecahedron or truncated icosahedron explode to form the great rhombicosidodecahedron (*bottom right*).

 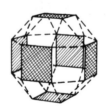 

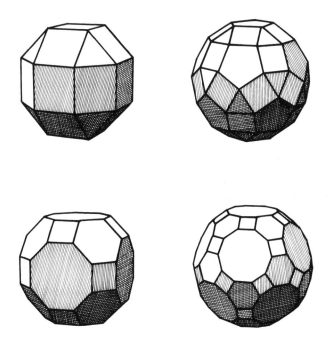

TURNING

The last two solids in this book are the snub cube (*top*) and the snub dodecahedron (*bottom*). 'Snub cube' is a loose translation of '*cubus simus*', literally 'the squashed cube'. Both of these solids possess a remarkable quality. They each have two versions, left and right-handed. The illustrations are both of the right-handed versions. The left-handed snub cube is shown on the front cover.

Remember the twist that transformed the cuboctahedron into the icosahedron (*page 46*)? Applying the corresponding twist to the rhombicuboctahedron produces the snub cube. Twist one way to make the right-handed version, and the other to make the left-handed one. Similarly the rhombicosidodecahedron twists to become the snub dodecahedron.

Of the solids in this book the snub dodecahedron is the closest to the sphere.

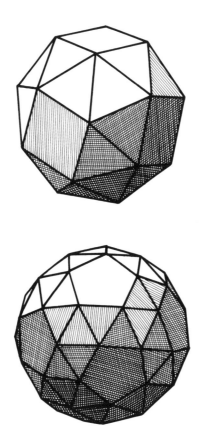

CONSTRUCTION NETS

If a solid is 'undone' along its edges and folded flat, the result is known as its net. These pages show the nets of the Platonic and Archimedian solids. They can be enlarged, cut out, and refolded to make the solids. Alternatively, to make a more permanent model, enlarge the nets, cut each face from a heavy card, and join the faces along their edges with a contact adhesive.

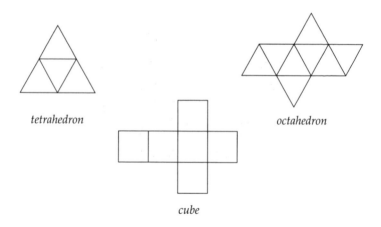

tetrahedron

octahedron

cube

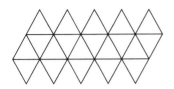

icosahedron

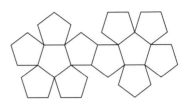

dodecahedron

truncated tetrahedron

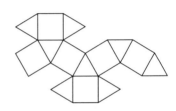

cuboctahedron

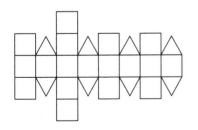

rhombicuboctahedron

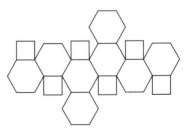

truncated octahedron

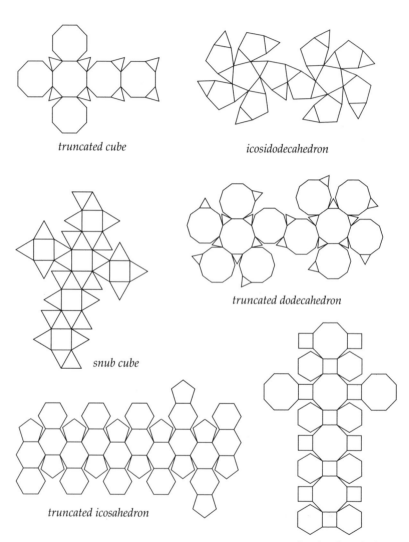

truncated cube

icosidodecahedron

snub cube

truncated dodecahedron

truncated icosahedron

great rhombicuboctahedron

56

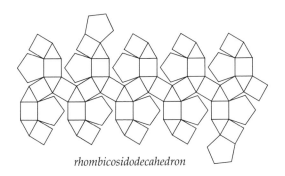

rhombicosidodecahedron

snub dodecahedron

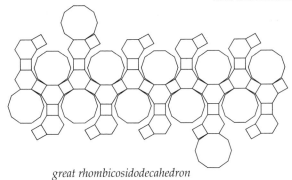

great rhombicosidodecahedron

57

DATA TABLE

All the data shown here is for solids fitted inside a sphere of radius 1, every vertex just touching its surface. This sphere is known as the circumsphere of the solid. The intersphere of a solid is the sphere that just touches the midpoints of its edges. The insphere of a solid is the sphere that just fits inside its faces.

Note that when their circumsphere is the same, the octahedron and the cube also have the same insphere. Likewise, the icosahedron and the dodecahedron also have the same insphere to circumsphere ratio.

The Archimedean solids have an insphere for each type of face. It is the value for the smallest insphere, touching the widest faces, which is shown opposite.

Solid	No. of vertices, edges & faces			Edge length	Intersphere radius	Insphere radius
Tetrahedron	4	6	4	1.633	0.577	0.333
Octahedron	6	12	8	1.414	0.707	0.577
Cube	8	12	6	1.155	0.817	0.577
Icosahedron	12	30	20	1.052	0.851	0.795
Dodecahedron	20	30	12	0.714	0.934	0.795
Trunc. Tetrahedron	12	18	8	0.853	0.905	0.522
Cuboctahedron	12	24	14	1	0.866	0.707
Rhombicuboctahedron	24	48	26	0.715	0.934	0.863
Trunc. Octahedron	24	36	14	0.632	0.949	0.775
Trunc. Cube	24	36	14	0.562	0.960	0.679
Trunc. Cuboctahedron	48	72	26	0.431	0.976	0.826
Snub Cube	24	60	38	0.744	0.928	0.850
Trunc. Icosahedron	60	90	32	0.404	0.979	0.915
Icosidodecahedron	30	60	32	0.618	0.951	0.851
Trunc. Dodecahedron	60	90	32	0.337	0.986	0.839
Rhombicosidodecahedron	60	120	62	0.448	0.975	0.925
Trunc. Icosidodecahedron	120	180	62	0.263	0.991	0.905
Snub Dodecahedron	60	150	92	0.464	0.972	0.918

If you have enjoyed this book, Professor Keith Critchlow's 'Order in Space' is highly recommended. 'Islamic Patterns' by the same author also has a good section on the Platonic Solids. Both books are published by Thames & Hudson.

Desmond Lee's translation of Plato's 'Timaeus' is both enjoyable and accessible, published by Penguin.

Another book in this series, 'Sacred Geometry' by Miranda Lundy, covers the unfolding of number in two-dimensional space.

For those who are mathematically inclined, and also keen on making models of the solids the following two books are recommended: "Shapes, Space and Symmetry" by Alan Holden, published by Dover and "Mathematical Models" by Cundy & Rollet, published by Tarquin Books.